KT-372-050

Uncle Aidan Goes Home

Written by Marie Dunleavy

BAINTE DEN STOC

WITHDRAWN FROM
DÚN LAOGHAIRE RATHDOWN COUNTY
LIBRARY STOCK

POPS
Resources

It was the end of Uncle Aidan's holiday.

He had to go home.

The children were sad.

They liked to play with Uncle Aidan.

Uncle Aidan asked the children to help him pack his bags.

Uncle Aidan had lots of clothes.

Milly put a jumper and a scarf into Uncle Aidan's bag.

She put a doll in too!

doll   jumper   scarf

Milly put some trousers into Uncle Aidan's bag.

Kal put some socks into a bag.

He put a ball in too!

trousers   socks   bag

Kal wanted to close Uncle
Aidan's bag.

It was too full.

Kal sat on it!

sat   full   close

Mum came to help.

She wanted to close the bags.

She took all the toys out.

close   bags   Mum

Dad put the bags in the car.

Then everyone went to the airport.

airport   bags   everyone

Uncle Aidan was going to fly home on a big plane.

Everyone said goodbye to Uncle Aidan.

The children were sad.

plane   goodbye   going

Mum said they could go to a café for lunch.

The children liked going out for lunch.

They were happy again!

café   lunch   going

POP it on!

scarf <small>UNCLE AIDAN GOES HOME</small>	**goodbye** <small>UNCLE AIDAN GOES HOME</small>
close <small>UNCLE AIDAN GOES HOME</small>	**airport** <small>UNCLE AIDAN GOES HOME</small>
socks <small>UNCLE AIDAN GOES HOME</small>	**sat** <small>UNCLE AIDAN GOES HOME</small>

doll

plane

UNCLE AIDAN GOES HOME

café

jumper

UNCLE AIDAN GOES HOME

everyone

going

UNCLE AIDAN GOES HOME

19

Find the word

Kal put some _____

Kal _____ on the

Dad put the _____

The children saw t

sat

UNCLE AIDAN GOES HOME

bags

UNCLE AIDAN GOES HOME

into the bag.

bag.

in the car.

big _____ .

plane	socks
UNCLE AIDAN GOES HOME	UNCLE AIDAN GOES HOME

Well done!

Match the Picture

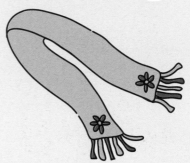

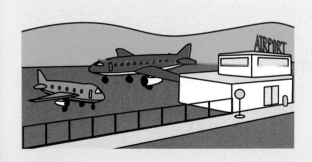

(Answers: plane, scarf, bag, socks; doll, café, airport, jumper)

Developing Reading Skills

POPS Books engage your child's interest whilst teaching your child to read in small easy steps. Each book introduces a prescribed number of words. Oval topic indicators (see below) indicate the word groups covered by each book.

Tips to get the most from this book:

* Give your child time to examine the illustrations and to discuss the story content.

* Ask your child to find the little blue elephant hidden on each page, and give them lots of praise.

* Allow your child to set the pace: encourage them to read the book independently when they indicate they are ready to do so.

* Supply any words your child is having difficulty with, so that the flow of the story is not lost.

POPS Word Cards offer repetition and consolidation through play:

* Match the POPS Word Cards to the words at the bottom of each text page.

* Use the Word Cards to play the games at the back of each book.

For further help, please download our free Teacher's and Parent's Manual at:

www.popsresources.com

Dressing   Actions